JUDGE DREDD

Featuring Judge Death

John Wagner
&
Brian Bolland

TITAN BOOKS

in association with *2000 AD*

Created in 1977 by writer John Wagner and artist Carlos Ezquerra, few comic strips have had the long-lasting appeal of *Judge Dredd*; which, given its subject matter – an overcrowded, ultra-violent city of the future, patrolled by lawmen ("Judges") empowered to act as on-the-spot judge, jury and executioner – is perhaps a little surprising. Although Dredd's early appearances, scripted by John Wagner, Pat Mills and others, and drawn by Ezquerra, instantly endeared the character to an entire generation of readers, it was the combined artistic efforts of Mike McMahon and, later, Brian Bolland, which established Dredd as an all-time comics icon.

McMahon's innovations – the "big booted" look with granite jaw, vast shoulder-pads, and unremitting scowl – were built on by Bolland, who used clean, bold inking to fine-line the jaw and other detail-work, altering the Dredd look from McMahon's often impressionistic style to a more accessible, 'grittier' realism, which still characterises Dredd to this day. Bolland, however, is quick to downplay his contribution:

"...I suppose I completely aped Mike's genius, the cleverness of his ideas, and then reinterpreted them in a style which actually borrowed a lot from the work of the American artists I was looking at."[1]

The editorial team at *2000 AD* clearly begged to differ, and Bolland was invited back to draw the historic cover for *2000 AD* Prog (issue) 2000, published in 1999.

What is incontrovertible is the breakthrough that constituted the 'Judge Death' storyline, and Bolland's devastatingly effective portrayal of both Judge Death and the other Dark Judges – Fear, Fire and Mortis. Bolland's Judge Death is a truly memorable villain, his costume a hideous parody of Dredd's, the rictus of his face ever-grinning, baleful as a gargoyle. A fitting nemesis for the ultimate Judge – or perhaps even a dark reflection.

Ironically for such an influential artist, Bolland has often found drawing a difficult and lengthy process, which might perhaps explain why he now almost exclusively produces cover art:

"I am slow, I'm very slow, and that's partly why I do covers... on *Judge Dredd* I was churning out these eight page stories in around two to three weeks, which wasn't exactly fast... it took me twelve hours just to ink a page..."[2]

Time well spent.

[1] Artists on Comics Art pg. 12, Mark Salisbury, Titan Books, 2000.
[2] Ibid, pp. 13 and 16.

This book, featuring Bolland's more self-contained *2000 AD* work (he also contributed to several of the longer *Dredd* stories, including classics like *The Cursed Earth*, *Judge Caligula* and *The Judge Child Quest*), and scripted by John Wagner[3], collects the following stories:

'Judge Death'

(Progs 149 - 151, January 26th - February 9th 1980)

A dark Judge from another dimension menaces Mega-City One; this story introduces Judge Death and Judge Anderson, Psi Division, who became a star in her own right.

'Judge Death Lives!'

(Progs 224 - 228, August 8th 1981 - 5th September 1981)

Death returns, with friends : can even Dredd stop him? This story introduces the three other dark Judges : Fear, Fire and Mortis.

'The First Lunar Olympics'

(Prog 50, February 5th 1978)

A cautionary, yet sadly prescient tale of future-sport and future-cheating.

'War Games'

(Prog 51, February 11th 1978)

Wagner and Bolland's take on the future of 'limited war'.

'The Oxygen Board'

(Prog 57, March 25th 1978)

A classic Dredd tale, with a typically sardonic Wagner twist ending.

'The Face-Change Crimes'

(Prog 52, February 18th 1978)

Showcases Bolland's genius for caricature.

'The Fog'

(Prog 127, August 25th 1979)

Wagner and Bolland revisit the classic 50s shocker, *House of Wax*, for this tenebrous tale.

'The Forever Crimes'

(Prog 120, July 7th 1979)

Dredd proves that even in death, there is no escape from the law...

'Punks Rule!'

(Prog 110, April 28th 1979)

In the aftermath of *Judge Caligula*, Dredd must restore order to Mega-City One... even if he has to do so single-handed!

---

[3] Wagner commonly wrote 2000 AD stories under pseudonyms such as "T.B. Grover" and "John Howard".

JUDGE DREDD

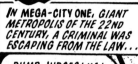

IN MEGA-CITY ONE, GIANT METROPOLIS OF THE 22ND CENTURY, A CRIMINAL WAS ESCAPING FROM THE LAW...

DUMB JUDGES! HA! THEY'LL NEVER CATCH TINY THE TAP!

2000 A.D.
Credit Card:
SCRIPT ROBOT
JOHN HOWARD
ART ROBOT
BRIAN BOLLAND
LETTERING ROBOT
TOM FRAME
COMPU·73E

ULP! ME AN' MY BIG MOUTH! I-I SURRENDER, JUDGE!

SATAN'S BREATH — Y-YOUR FACE! YOU-YOU'RE NO ORDINARY JUDGE! YOU—

M-MY DOK!

H-HIS HAND...

...G-G-GOING RIGHT INTO ME!

MY NAME ISS DEATH. I HAVE COME TO JUDGE YOU!

UGH!

JUDGE DEATH PART 1

WHEN THE BODY WAS FOUND, TOP LAWMAN JUDGE DREDD WAS CALLED IN —

IT'S TINY THE TAP! WE WERE CHASING HIM WHEN WE LOST HIM IN THIS MAZE.

WHEN WE FOUND HIM HE WAS DEAD. THERE'S NOT A MARK ON HIM — BUT LOOK AT HIS FACE!

LIKE HE DIED OF... TERROR!

NO SIGN OF ANY ATTACKER, BUT WE FOUND THIS UNDER TINY'S NAILS. COULD BE SKIN TISSUE. PONGS A BIT!

THERE'S A STRANGE SMELL OF DECAY ALL AROUND HERE. OKAY, RUN THAT DOWN TO THE LAB. I'LL GET A SEARCH SQUAD OUT.

SOON, AT THE LAB —

SKIN, ALL RIGHT. MIGHT BE HUMAN — HARD TO TELL JUST YET. IT'S IN AN ADVANCED STATE OF DECOMPOSITION...

I'M NOT TALKING ABOUT DAYS, OR EVEN YEARS. THIS SKIN HAS BEEN DEAD FOR *CENTURIES*.

IMPOSSIBLE. IF THE SKIN ISN'T TINY'S, IT'S GOT TO BE HIS ATTACKER'S.

THEN ALL I CAN SAY IS — WE'VE GOT A MIGHTY STRANGE KILLER WALKING THIS CITY!

HE HEARD THE SOUND ECHOING THROUGH THE CONCRETE CAVERNS OF THE CITY. IT DREW HIM LIKE A MAGNET...

THE ONE SOUND WHICH COULD STIR FEELING IN THAT COLD, DEAD HEART. THE SOUND OF LAUGHTER...OF LIFE...

THAT HATED SOUND!

MORE SCROTNIG SOUNDS COMIN' ROUND FROM THE GUY WITH THE 'LECTRIC EYES! RIGHT NOW PLUG INTO THE NUMBER ONE BLAST — *WHO PUT THE BOOP?!!*

♪ *WHO PUT THE BOOP ON MY BEST BROWN BOOTS?* ♫ *WHO PUT THE GLOP ON MY ZIGGA ZIGGA ZING ZANG?*

HEY-EY! THE SOUND ABOUNDS!

OH MY SOUL!

MY NAME ISS DEATH. I HAVE COME TO JUDGE YOU.

MY GRUD! WHAT- WHAT IS IT?

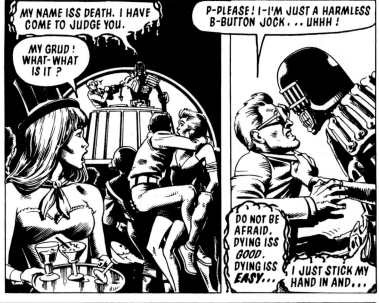

P-PLEASE! I-I'M JUST A HARMLESS B-BUTTON JOCK... UHHH!

DO NOT BE AFRAID. DYING ISS GOOD. DYING ISS EASY...

I JUST STICK MY HAND IN AND...

SSQUEEZZE!

CONTROL TO DREDD! SOUNDS OF DISTRESS HEARD COMING FROM THE RABBIT HUTCH. COULD BE YOUR MAN!

WE'RE ON OUR WAY!

SOON—

HELP!

DOORS ARE LOCKED! BREAK THEM OPEN!

INSIDE—

DOK! WHAT A NIGHTMARE!

THERE'S THAT STENCH OF DECAY!

NEXT PROG: **THE GUILTY... AND THE DAMNED!**

WHATEVER *ELSE* IT IS, THAT THING'S *NOT* HUMAN!

AS THE FLAMES DIED...

JUST A CHARRED HUSK! HE'S NOT COMING BACK TO LIFE AFTER *THAT!*

THERE'S SMOKE RISING FROM ITS HEAD!

AND THERE'S THAT FOUL STENCH AGAIN!

DOK! LOOK AT IT!

IT'S GETTING THICKER!

LAWBREAKERS! YOU HAVE *DELAYED* ME, THAT ISS ALL. THISS CCITY ISS EVIL, BUT *I* WILL CLEANSSE IT!

ALL WILL BE JUDGED!

AND THEN IT WAS GONE... LEAVING ONLY THE SHATTERED RUIN OF THE NIGHTCLUB AND THE BODIES OF THE JUDGED...

IT JUST *BLEW AWAY!* MY GRUD, DREDD, WHAT KIND OF MONSTER *IS* THIS?

I WISH I KNEW, McKAY.

THERE'S TOO MUCH WE DON'T KNOW ABOUT *JUDGE DEATH.* WE'D BETTER START FINDING OUT, AND QUICK. IT DOESN'T LOOK LIKE HE'S TAKING ANY PRISONERS!

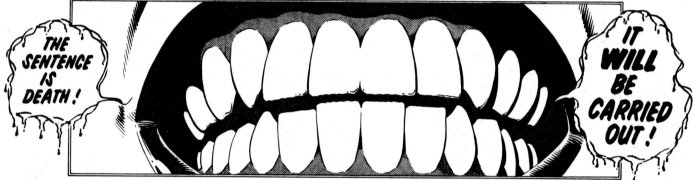

THARG NOTE: BOING — SEE PROG 136.

NOW, DREDD! DO IT — THE BOING TIN !

THE MIRACLE PLASTIC SWELLED AROUND ANDERSON —

GRUD! WHAT ON EARTH — ?

YOU CAN'T KILL DEATH. WE HAD TO TRAP HIM. THERE WAS ONLY ONE WAY, AND ANDERSON REALISED IT...

HE'S TRAPPED IN ANDERSON'S HEAD — ENCASED IN... BOING!

WE CAN'T EVER RISK JUDGE DEATH BREAKING FREE. ANDERSON CAN NEVER COME OUT OF THERE... AND SHE KNEW IT. HER BRAVERY WILL BE REMEMBERED!

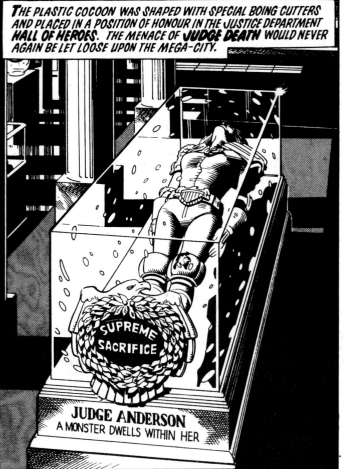

THE PLASTIC COCOON WAS SHAPED WITH SPECIAL BOING CUTTERS AND PLACED IN A POSITION OF HONOUR IN THE JUSTICE DEPARTMENT HALL OF HEROES. THE MENACE OF JUDGE DEATH WOULD NEVER AGAIN BE LET LOOSE UPON THE MEGA-CITY.

SUPREME SACRIFICE

JUDGE ANDERSON
A MONSTER DWELLS WITHIN HER

HE'S GONE !
BETTER MOVE
FAST !

HEAT SENSORS REGISTERING SHARP
INCREASE IN THE **ANDERSON ANNEXE** !
COULD BE **FIRE** !

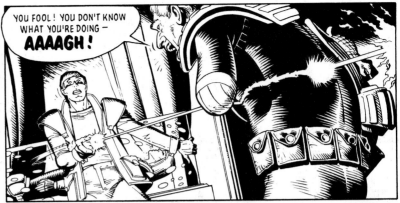

I... MUST HAVE MISCOUNTED THE NUMBERS COMING OUT!

NOT GOOD ENOUGH, STURMEY. YOUR NEGLIGENCE MAY HAVE COST THE CITY DEAR. PLACE YOURSELF UNDER DETENTION.

FOUR THOUSAND TOURISTS VISIT THE HALL OF HEROES EACH DAY —

I WANT THEM CHECKED — EVERY ONE OF THEM. INFORM THE CHIEF JUDGE WE'VE GOT A LEVEL ONE EMERGENCY ON OUR HANDS.

WE'VE GOT TO CATCH THIS CREEP BEFORE ALL HELL BREAKS LOOSE!

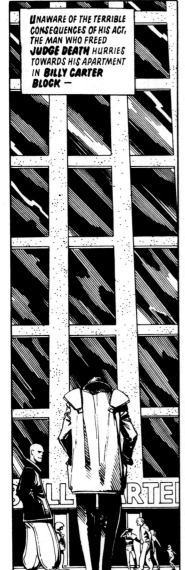

UNAWARE OF THE TERRIBLE CONSEQUENCES OF HIS ACT, THE MAN WHO FREED JUDGE DEATH HURRIES TOWARDS HIS APARTMENT IN BILLY CARTER BLOCK —

APT 1027B

J-JANINE!

YOU PROMISED! YOU PROMISED YOU W-WOULDN'T KILL HER IF I HELPED YOU!

WE LIED!

THE FOETID TOUCH OF JUDGE MORTIS BRINGS... DECAY!

THE BODY ISS RIPE! LET THE DEAD FLUIDS FLOW OVER IT!

OUTSIDE THE GRAND HALL OF JUSTICE —

JUDGE DREDD, YOU'RE HEADING THE SEARCH! JUST WHAT HARM CAN THIS MONSTER DO?

ACCORDING TO THE WARPED LOGIC OF HIS DIMENSION, ALL CRIME IS COMMITTED BY THE LIVING — THEREFORE LIFE ITSELF IS A CRIME.

AS LONG AS JUDGE DEATH IS AT LARGE, NO CITIZEN IS SAFE!

BUT YOU SAY HE'S IN SOME KIND OF... SPIRIT FORM?

HE CAN CREATE ANOTHER BODY. HE WILL TRY TO. THAT'S ENOUGH QUESTIONS!

ATTENTION, JUDGE DREDD! SOMETHING INTERESTING HERE! ONE OF THE HALL OF HEROES TOURISTS IS REGISTERED AS HAVING STRONG TELEPATHIC POTENTIAL — POSSIBLY A CARRIER FOR JUDGE DEATH!

NAME OF MITSON. APARTMENT 1027b, BILLY CARTER BLOCK.

ON MY WAY!

IN THE BILLY CARTER BLOCK, THE HORRIFYING TRANSFORMATION WAS NEARING COMPLETION —

ENTER, DEATH! FILL THISS SOULLESS CARCASS!

THE MANHOLE'S NO GOOD, DREDD! THEIR SHIELD GOES RIGHT UNDER THE WHOLE BLOCK!

I CAN GET YOU THROUGH IT, DREDD!

ANDERSON OF PSI-DIVISION – JUDGES SPECIALLY TRAINED FOR THEIR ABNORMAL PSYCHIC POWER –

THAT'S A PSI-SHIELD! THEY'RE USING SOME KIND OF PSYCHIC WAVE GENERATOR! THE ONLY WAY THROUGH IS TO DEFLECT THE WAVES!

AND YOU RECKON YOU CAN DO IT?

FOR MANY MONTHS THE SPIRIT OF JUDGE DEATH HAS DWELT WITHIN ANDERSON –

YOU DON'T HAVE A RAT LIKE DEATH CAMPING OUT IN YOUR BRAIN WITHOUT PICKING UP A FEW TRICKS! I KNOW I CAN DO IT! COME ON!

HOLD TIGHT – WE'RE GOING THROUGH!

THEN EVERY OUNCE OF ANDERSON'S MENTAL POWER IS FOCUSSED AGAINST THE PSI-SHIELD –

GOT TO... FORCE... IT... OPEN!

WE'RE THROUGH! GOOD WORK, ANDERSON!

AND IN PEANUT PARK –

ANDERSSON!

DEATH

NEXT PROG: FACE TO FACE WITH FEAR!

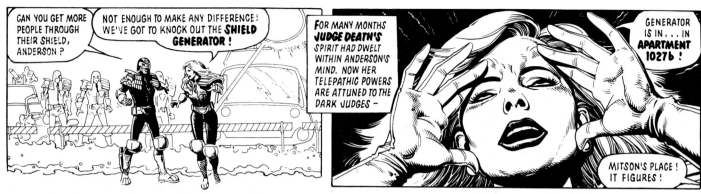

CAN YOU GET MORE PEOPLE THROUGH THEIR SHIELD, ANDERSON?

NOT ENOUGH TO MAKE ANY DIFFERENCE! WE'VE GOT TO KNOCK OUT THE SHIELD GENERATOR!

FOR MANY MONTHS JUDGE DEATH'S SPIRIT HAD DWELT WITHIN ANDERSON'S MIND. NOW HER TELEPATHIC POWERS ARE ATTUNED TO THE DARK JUDGES—

GENERATOR IS IN... IN APARTMENT 1027b!

MITSON'S PLACE! IT FIGURES!

JUDGE DREDD! THANK GOD YOU'VE COME!

DON'T COUNT YOUR CHICKENS YET, CITIZEN!

JUDGE FIRE IS CLOSE — I CAN SENSE HIM!

BACK!

BOING WORKED ON DEATH! LET'S SEE HOW THIS CREEP LIKES IT!

YOU'RE WASTING YOUR TIME, DREDD!

BOING®, THE MIRACLE PLASTIC, HAD ONCE TRAPPED JUDGE DEATH—

ON JUDGE FIRE, IT IS USELESS!

IT'S IGNITING!

FOOLSS! YOU DARE TO RESISST USS — YOU, WHO HAVE FAILED IN YOUR DUTY TO JUDGE YOUR OWN PEOPLE!

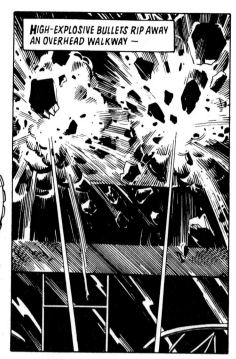

NEXT PROG: DEATH'S DARK DOMINION!

SCRIPT
T. B. GROVER
ART
BRIAN BOLLAND
LETTERING
T FRAME

THE FOUR DARK JUDGES — **FEAR, FIRE, DEATH** AND **MORTIS** — HAVE ARRIVED FROM ANOTHER DIMENSION TO JUDGE THE MEGA-CITY. NOW **DREDD** AND **ANDERSON** HAVE DESTROYED THE SHIELD AROUND THE BILLY CARTER BLOCK, WHERE THE DARK JUDGES HAVE BEEN DISPENSING THEIR BRUTAL JUSTICE —

HIT BILLY CARTER BLOCK WITH EVERYTHING YOU'VE GOT!

JUDGE DEATH LIVES

CONCLUSION

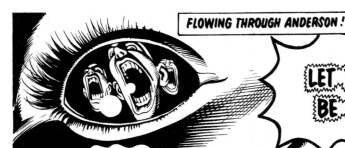

FLOWING THROUGH ANDERSON!

LET THE JUDGES BE JUDGED!

YOU ARE GUILTY!

THE SENTENCE IS DEATH!

DEATH!

As THE SPIRITS OF THE FOUR DARK JUDGES ARE EXTINGUISHED, THE DEAD CARCASSES THAT HOUSE THEM — **CRUMBLE**!

IT'S OVER, DREDD! THEY'LL NEVER TROUBLE US AGAIN!

THEY'RE STILL TROUBLING ME! GIVE ME A HAND WITH THIS PITCHFORK, ANDERSON!

AFTER THIS, I THINK I'LL PUT IN FOR THAT SICK LEAVE!

AFTER THIS, I MAY JUST JOIN YOU, ANDERSON!

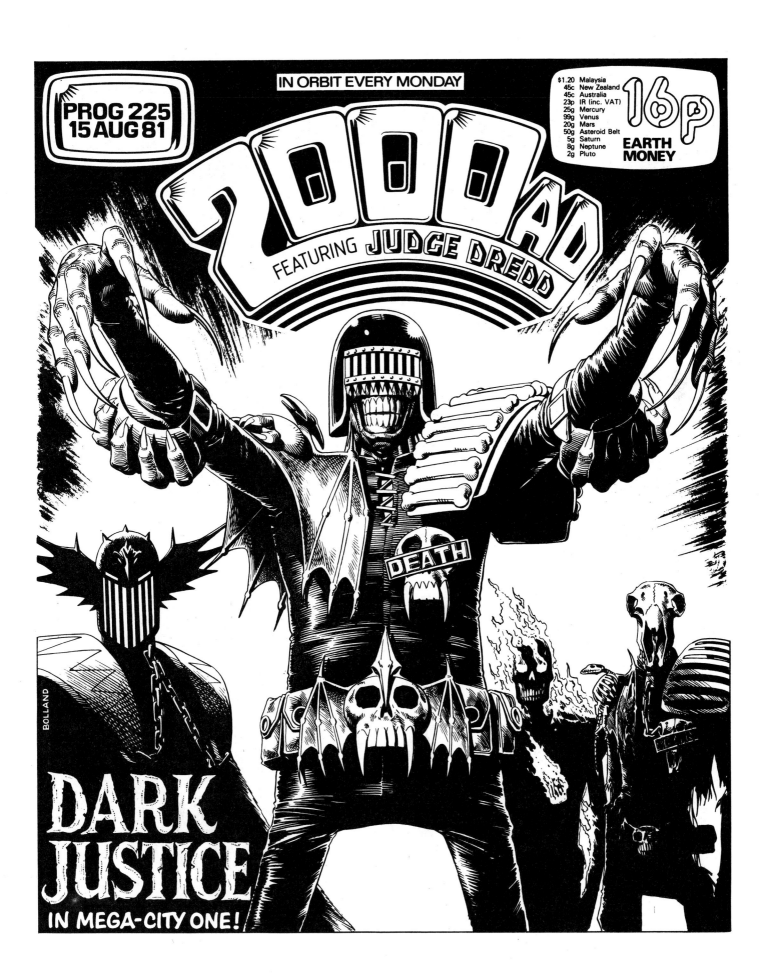

2000 A.D.
Credit Card:

SCRIPT ROBOT
JOHN WAGNER

ART ROBOT
BRIAN BOLLAND

LETTERING ROBOT
TONY JACOB

COMPU·73E

NEXT MORNING JUDGE DREDD, IN CHARGE OF SECURITY FOR THE GAMES, VISITS THE ATHLETES' INSPECTION AREA BENEATH THE STADIUM...

I PROTEST! THIS IS A LUNA-1 TRICK TO DISCREDIT THE SOV-CITIES TEAM!

COSMOVICH AND KOLB, THE SOV-CITIES JUDGES IN CHARGE OF THEIR TEAM. MAKING TROUBLE, AS USUAL.

THE SPECTRO-SCAN SHOWS STEROIDS, ILLEGAL DRUGS, IN THE ATHLETE'S BODY...

THE RED AREAS SHOW STEROIDS, ILLEGAL BODY-BUILDING DRUGS. THE BLUE AND GREEN ONES ARE STANIMINE, FOR STAMINA.

THAT GUY'S A WALKING DRUG STORE!

THE SOVS ARE TOUCHY, AND WE DON'T WANT AN INTERNATIONAL INCIDENT. TRY HIM ON A BIO-SCAN.

"TEN SOMERSAULTS, PIKED, WITH HYPER-TWIST! THIS IS A BRILLIANT RUN BY BONNARD!"

"BUT HE'S GOT TOO MUCH SPEED ON — THE BRITISH BOY IS GOING TO . . .

. . . MISS THE CATCH NETS!"

AAARGH!

JUDGES

OH, DEAR, THAT LANDING'S GOING TO COST HIM MARKS!

3·6 2·5 4·7 2·0 1·8 2·1 2·2 3·0

BY THE END OF THE WEEK A TENSE SITUATION HAS BUILT UP . . .

"YES, FOLKS, THE MEDAL TABLE STANDS AT 24 GOLDS TO SOV-CITIES, 24 TO LUNA-1! IT ALL DEPENDS ON THE LAST RACE — THE 100 METRES SPRINT!"

GOLD TABLE
SOV-CITIES
LUNAR 1
BRIT-TER
-SLES

"THE COMPETITORS ARE ON THEIR BLOCKS! THERE IN LANE 1 IS NICOLAI ZILCH FOR SOV-CITIES! ZILCH'S BIONIC THIGHS GIVE TREMENDOUS STARTING THRUST, AND . . ."

OFFICIAL

"IN LANE 3 — TYRONE J. TYRONE, LUNA-1. THAT STREAMLINED SKULL IS A RESULT OF TWO YEARS' CYBO-SURGERY!"

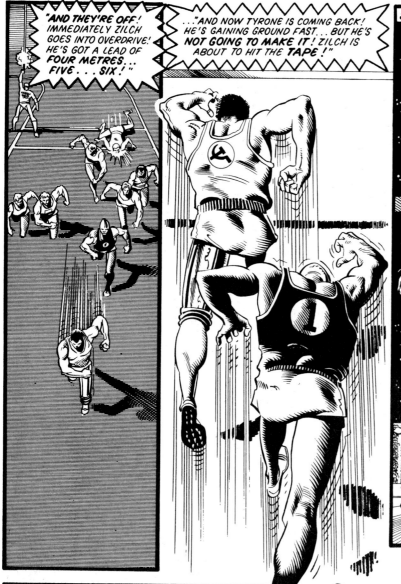

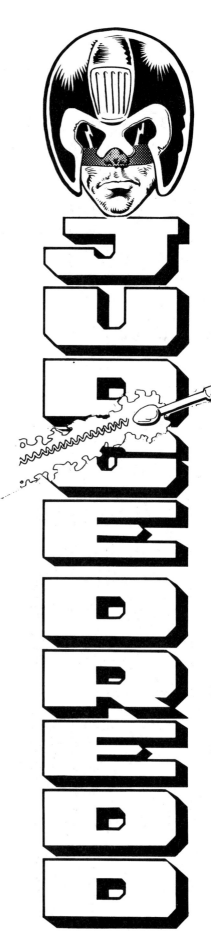

DIRECT HIT! NOTHING'S GETTING UP FROM THAT!

AARRGGH!

BUT...

THIS IS INCREDIBLE, FOLKS! THE SOV-CITIES' SOLDIER IS GETTING UP! THE BOMB HASN'T EVEN DENTED THE NEW SOV ANTI-BLAST SUIT!

NEXT SECOND...

DIE, DOG!

AAAGH!

THEY GOT AL!

D-DID YOU SEE THAT? THAT ELECTRO BEAM WENT RIGHT THROUGH TWO FEET OF CONCRETE AND EXPLODED INSIDE AL'S SUIT!

SHOEMAKER

BROWN

THE SOVS GOT WEAPONS AND ARMOUR LIKE WE'VE NEVER DREAMED OF. I...I'M GONNA CALL A TIME OUT, DEL.

AND SO...

NOW WHILE THE MEN ARE SORTING THEMSELVES OUT, LET ME EXPLAIN THE RULES OF THE WAR FOR VIEWERS WHO'VE JUST SWITCHED ON...

UMPIRE

AS YOU PROBABLY KNOW, WARS TODAY ARE NO LONGER FOUGHT BETWEEN VAST ARMIES, BUT BY COMBAT UNITS CONSISTING OF FOUR SOLDIERS AND ONE RESERVE!

SO, WHEN ONE SIDE HAS BEEN WIPED OUT, THE OTHER SIDE WINS! THEY ARE THEN ENTITLED TO CLAIM TERRITORY FROM THE LOSING NATION!

JUDGE DREDD WAS LUNA-1 OBSERVER AT THE WAR...

YES, FOLKS, GONE ARE THE DAYS WHEN MILLIONS DIED ON THE BATTLEFIELD! THIS IS **GOOD WAR-CLEAN WAR**! SO SIT BACK IN YOUR SEATS AND **ENJOY THE ACTION**!

WE'RE NO BETTER THAN THE SOVS. THEY USE WAR AS AN EXCUSE TO GRAB LAND— WE TREAT IT AS A **GAME**!

JUDGE DREDD-LOOK! A **HYPO-DART** IN OUR RESERVE'S NECK! HE'S OUT FOR THE COUNT.

I BET THOSE **STINKIN' SOVS** DID IT. IT AIN'T ENOUGH THAT THEY GOT **BETTER WEAPONS** THAN US...

TELL YOUR MEN TO **SURRENDER**, DREDD. CONCEDE YOUR APOLLO TERRITORY TO US AND SOV-CITIES WILL BE SATISFIED.

YOUR TYPE ARE **NEVER SATISFIED**, COSMOVICH. IF WE DON'T PUT YOU DOWN NOW, YOU'LL TRY THE SAME TRICK AGAIN.

TAKE OFF WALLY'S GEAR, IKE. **YOU JUST GOT YOUR-SELF ANOTHER RESERVE**.

THE COMBAT UNITS ARE COMING OUT TO RESUME FIGHTING! WITH LUNA-1 RESERVE...HEY...THAT'S NOT THE RESERVE... **IT'S JUDGE DREDD!**

...THEY GOTTA FIX IT SO WE HAVE TO FIGHT 'EM WITH **ONLY TWO MEN**!

UNDER THE RULES OF THE WAR EACH MAN MUST RETURN TO THE POSITION OCCUPIED BEFORE TIME OUT WAS CALLED. DREDD JOINED THE TWO SOLDIERS IN THE BATTERED BUILDING...

PHEEEEP!

THERE'S THE WHISTLE! GIVE 'EM EVERYTHING YOU'VE GOT, BOYS!

WASTE BULLETS, FOOLS! NOTHING CAN PENETRATE OUR BLAST-SUITS!

I HAVE THEM ON INFRA-RED. RANGE 35. **FIRING!**

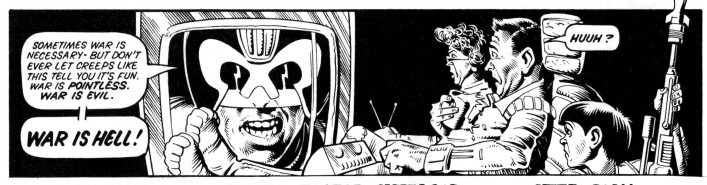

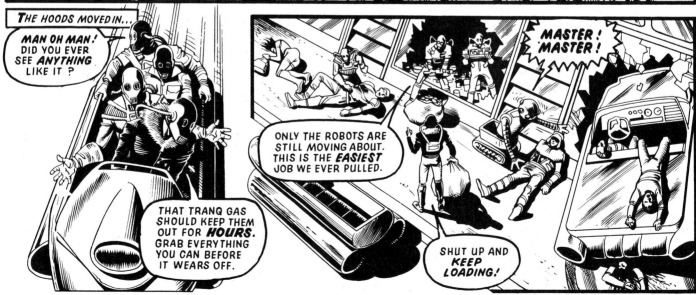

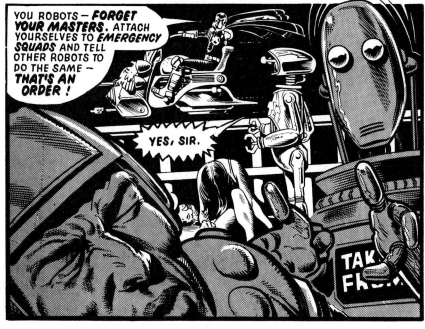

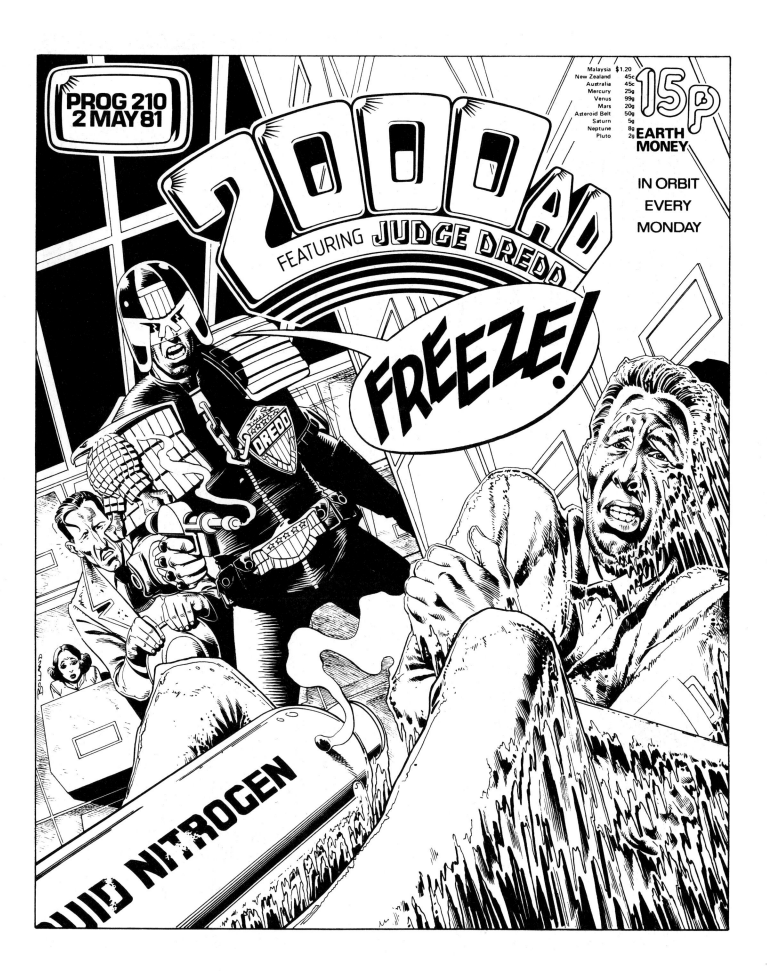

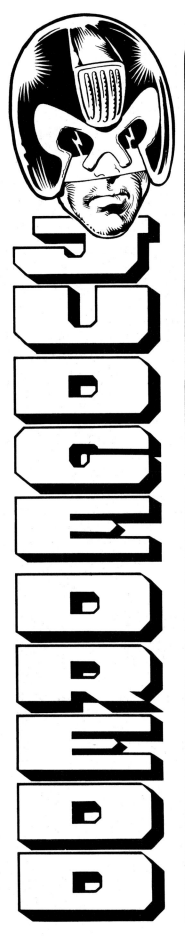

BY THE TIME JUDGE DREDD, MARSHAL OF LUNA-1, HAD ARRIVED ON THE SCENE, A CORDON HAD BEEN SET UP ROUND THE BANK...

FIRST LUNAR BANK

THEY'RE HOLDING HOSTAGES IN THE BANK. THIS IS A PHOTOGRAPH THE SECURITY COMPUTER GOT OF THEM BEFORE THEY PUT IT OUT OF ACTION.

HMMM... SOMETHING FAMILIAR ABOUT THESE CREEPS. BUT I CAN'T PUT NAMES TO THE FACES...

YOU MEN IN THERE! GIVE YOURSELVES UP!

NO WAY! WE FIGHT IT OUT TO THE END. BUT WE'RE NOT HEARTLESS — WE'RE SENDING THE HOSTAGES OUT FOR SAFETY!

ONE BY ONE THE HOSTAGES STAGGERED OUT TO WAITING AMBULANCES...

THAT'S THE LAST... GET THAT MACHINE WORKING QUICK. SET IT FOR NUMBER TWO DISGUISE!

ONLY THREE MORE TO COME, DREDD!

THE MACHINE WAS SWITCHED ON — AND A REMARKABLE CHANGE TOOK PLACE.

SECONDS LATER, OUTSIDE —

THAT'S THE LAST THREE. OKAY, MEN, HIT 'EM WITH THOSE SMOKE BOMBS.

AMBULANCE

AMBULANCE

THE BOMBS EXPLODED —

RUSH 'EM!

HUH? THERE'S NO-ONE HERE... BUT THAT'S IMPOSSIBLE!

I THOUGHT I RECOGNISED THOSE FACES — ALL *20TH CENTURY COMEDIANS.*

I—I DON'T UNDERSTAND, MARSHAL!

THEY'VE GOT A *FACE-CHANGER MACHINE.* WE WERE LOOKING FOR THE THREE MEN IN THE PHOTOGRAPH AND *NOW* THEY'RE GETTING AWAY IN ONE OF OUR *OWN* AMBULANCES! NOW...

THE PHOTOGRAPH... NOW IT'S ALL BEGINNING TO CLICK, LET ME SEE IT *AGAIN.*

INDEED, AT THAT MOMENT...

HONK! HONK!

HA, HA! SOON AS WE GET BACK TO THE APARTMENT WE STASH THE CASH AND CHANGE BACK TO OUR OWN FACES. IT'S *A PIECE OF CAKE.*

WE CAN AFFORD *A NIGHT AT THE OPERA* AFTER THIS!

FACE-CHANGING MACHINES WORKED ON THE PRINCIPLE OF MATTER REORGANISATION. NEXT DAY DREDD VISITED THE ONLY COMPANY ON LUNA-1 THAT SOLD THEM...

DREDD PORED OVER THE SALES BOOK UNTIL...

TOOLEY—AL TOOLEY. I MIGHT HAVE KNOWN! HE AND HIS BROTHERS, BRAD AND LAPSLEY, ARE THE BIGGEST CON-MEN IN THE BUSINESS. THE TROUBLE IS...

...PROVING THEY ROBBED THE BANK!

YESSIR, MARSHAL. WE CAN HAVE YOUR FACE CHANGED BY EXPERTS HERE IN OUR SALON, OR PERHAPS YOU'D PREFER OUR DO-IT-YOURSELF KIT? A NEW FACE FOR EVERY DAY!

I DON'T WANT MY FACE CHANGED, FOOL! I WANT THE NAMES OF ANYONE WHO'S BOUGHT ONE OF THESE WRETCHED MACHINES FROM YOU.

ON DREDD'S ORDERS THE TOOLEY BROTHERS WERE BROUGHT TO JUSTICE CENTRAL AND SUBJECTED TO AN INTENSE THREE-HOUR INTERROGATION BY JUDGES SPECIALLY TRAINED IN THE ART...

I'M STRAIGHT, I TELL YOU. I DON'T KNOW ANYTHING ABOUT A BANK JOB.

I WANT TO SEE MY LAWYER!

IT'S NO GOOD, MARSHAL. THEY WON'T TALK TILL THEY'VE SEEN THEIR LAWYER, MANNY BLOOM.

SPEAK OF THE DEVIL, HERE HE COMES NOW. THE CROOKEDEST LAWYER ON LUNA-1...

WHAT THE HECK IS THIS, DREDD? YOU CAN'T HOLD MY CLIENTS WITHOUT ANY EVIDENCE AGAINST THEM. I DEMAND YOU RELEASE THEM OR I'LL—

OKAY, MANNY, CALM DOWN. YOU CAN HAVE 'EM. THEY'RE MAKING A NASTY SMELL IN THE JUSTICE BUILDING.

KEEP CALM + + + THRILL FACTOR OVERLOAD + + +

FOG HAD COME TO MEGA-CITY ONE, 22ND CENTURY AMERICA'S VAST METROPOLIS OF OVER 800 MILLION PEOPLE. LIKE A SUFFOCATING BLANKET IT HUNG OVER WEATHER DISTRICT 6... BRINGING NEW DANGERS TO THE STREETS...

STAY IN YOUR HOMES... DO NOT GO OUT UNLESS IT IS ABSOLUTELY NECESSARY... WE ARE TRYING TO CORRECT THE FAULT IN YOUR WEATHER....

2000 A.D.
Credit Card:
SCRIPT ROBOT
JOHN HOWARD
ART ROBOT
BRIAN BOLLAND
LETTERING ROBOT
TOM FRAME
COMPU·73E

JUDGE DREDD

BUT NOT EVERYONE OBEYED THE WARNINGS OF THE JUDGES, THE MEN WHO KEPT LAW AND ORDER IN THE CITY.

'BYE, GIRLS.

DOK, WHAT WEATHER! IT REMINDS ME OF THE PEA-SOUPERS THEY USED TO HAVE IN OLD LONDON.

CAN'T WAIT TO GET HOME. THERE'VE BEEN SOME STRANGE DISAPPEARANCES SINCE THE FOG STARTED.

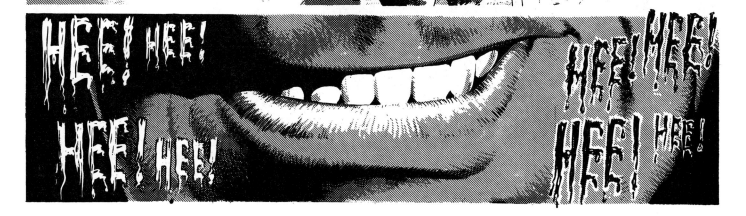

HEE! HEE! HEE! HEE! HEE! HEE! HEE! HEE! HEE! HEE!

THIS IS WHERE I TURN OFF. 'BYE, DOREEN... WATCH OUT FOR THE WEE GREEN MEN!

YOU'VE GOT A FUNNY SENSE OF HUMOUR, CAROL! 'BYE!

BUT AS DOREEN WALKED ON...

HEE! HEE! HEE! HEE!

HEE! HEE! HEE!

...SOMEONE COMING... WHO-WHO ARE YOU? WHAT DO YOU WANT?

I'VE COME FOR THE PIE-FILLING, ME DEAR!

N-NO... NO! SOMEONE HELP MEEEEE!

HEE, HEE, HEE!

THOUGHT I HEARD A CRY FOR HELP — OH, NO! DOREEN!

A MASSIVE EQUIPMENT FAILURE ABOVE DISTRICT G HAD CAUSED FREAK CONDITIONS. FOR OVER A WEEK WEATHER CONTROL HAD BEEN STRUGGLING TO REPAIR THE DAMAGE...

...WHILE ON THE STREETS BELOW, HIDDEN BY THE FOG, CRIME RAN WILD!

JUDGE DREDD, MEGA-CITY'S TOP JUDGE, WAS QUICKLY ON THE SCENE OF THE LATEST OUTRAGE —

AND THEN — THEN HE PICKED HER UP AND — AND RAN OFF! HE-HE WORE A-A BIG TOP HAT AND A BLACK CLOAK!

THAT COULD DESCRIBE TEN THOUSAND MEN IN THIS CITY! THINK HARDER, CITIZEN. WE'VE GOT TO CATCH THIS MANIAC BEFORE HE STRIKES AGAIN!

I WAS RIGHT — A ROBOT!

H'MM... CHAMBER OF HORRORS... THAT EXPLAINS A LOT OF QUESTIONS.

CHAMBER HORRORS

AFTER SUMMONING MEDICAL AID FOR THE SHOCKED DOREEN, DREDD MADE FOR THE MEGA-CITY CHAMBER OF HORRORS WHICH LAY IN THE MIDDLE OF THE FOG DISTRICT. THERE, ROBOTS HAD LONG AGO REPLACED LIFELESS WAXWORK MODELS —

THESE ROBOTS COULD BE BEHIND A LOT OF THE STRANGE THINGS THAT HAVE BEEN HAPPENING SINCE THE FOG...

FOOTSTEPS! SOMEONE'S COMING!

BODIES FOR GOLD, THAT'S WHIT HE SAID! BODIES FOR GOLD!

BURKE AND HARE, THE BODYSNATCHERS!

DREDD FOLLOWED THE MURDERERS —

NO! NO! **NO!** HOW MANY TIMES DO I HAVE TO TELL YOU TWO? *I SENT YOU OUT TO GET MONEY, NOT BODIES!*

BODIES FOR GOLD, YE SAID. IS THAT NO' RIGHT?

YES, YES, DAT'S WHAT HE SAID... BODIES FOR GOLD, DAT'S WHAT HE SAID ALL ROIGHT.

SHALL I LOP OFF THEIR VILLAINOUS HEADS, ME LUD?

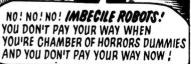

NO! NO! NO! *IMBECILE ROBOTS!* YOU DON'T PAY YOUR WAY WHEN YOU'RE CHAMBER OF HORRORS DUMMIES AND YOU DON'T PAY YOUR WAY NOW!

CRIME NEVER PAYS, CITIZEN! YOU'RE UNDER ARREST!

J-JUDGE DREDD! GET HIM!

DONNGG

THE BELLS! THE BELLS!

THEY'RE RINGING FOR *YOU*, PAL!

DREDD GRASPED THE ROPE AND SWUNG —

UGGH!

I'LL TAKE THAT FIREARM, CITIZEN!

THE FUN'S OVER, CITIZEN! I'M TAKING YOU IN!

OH, GOOD! CAN I COME DOWN NOW?

OTHER JUDGES WERE SOON ON THE SCENE —

I-I NEVER MEANT THEM TO KILL... THE CHAMBER OF HORRORS WAS LOSING MONEY, SO...SO WHEN THE FOG CAME, I CHANGED THEIR PROGRAMMES AND SENT THEM ONTO THE STREETS TO STEAL...

...BUT THEY COULDN'T DO ANYTHING RIGHT! THEY COULDN'T OVERCOME THEIR BASIC PROGRAMMING...

LOOKS LIKE THE FOG IS CLEARING AT LAST...

FOR YOU THE FOG IS ONLY STARTING, CITIZEN!

NEXT RROG: THE FOREVER CRIMES

IN THE YEAR 2101 THERE WILL STILL BE DISEASES THAT SCIENCE CANNOT CURE. BUT FOR SOME – THE VERY RICH – THERE WILL BE A WAY TO DEFEAT DEATH... A WAY TO SPIN THE LAST FEW HOURS OF LIFE INTO CENTURIES...

2000 A.D.
Credit Card:
SCRIPT ROBOT
JOHN HOWARD
ART ROBOT
BRIAN BOLLAND
LETTERING ROBOT
TOM FRAME
COMPU·73E

STOPPING THE SUSPENDED ANIMATION PROCESS, DR GOLD.

BRING HER UP TO MINIMUM LIFE TEMPERATURE, NURSE.

JUDGE DREDD

THE FOREVER CRIMES

MRS DREYFUS HAS ONLY TWO HOURS OF TOTAL LIFE TIME. I CAN'T LET YOU USE UP MORE THAN THREE MINUTES, JUDGE DREDD.

A GLIMMER OF LIFE FLICKERED IN THE WOMAN'S EYES...

JUDGE DREDD... THEN IT IS OVER. MY SON HAS... KILLED HIMSELF.

YOU EXPECTED IT? THEN PERHAPS YOU CAN TELL ME WHY HE TOOK HIS LIFE.

THAT'S ONE PIECE OF INFORMATION YOU'LL NEVER USE, DOCTOR!

JUDGE DREDD!

GAS POWER

OP-THEA

DON'T SH-SHOOT! I'LL COME QUIETLY —

A JET OF LIQUID CRYOGENIC GAS SHOT OUT OF THE MACHINE —

AAAH!

VISOR'S FROSTED OVER — I CAN'T SEE!

YOU'RE A BLIND MAN, DREDD: THIS IS PURE LIQUID NITROGEN! WITHOUT SPECIAL DRUGS YOU CAN'T SURVIVE A DIRECT BLAST!

AND I'LL FREEZE TO DEATH IF I STAY HERE MUCH LONGER!

YOU FORGET ONE THING — JUDGES DON'T NEED TO SEE!

THAT NIGHT, BEHIND THE COSMIC PUNKS' BARRICADE...

WORD IS THE JUDGES MIGHT HIT US TONIGHT. GESTAPO BOB SAYS TA KEEP YER BLASTER-FINGERS OILED.

NATCH, FILE-TOOTH.

HEY, I HEAR AN ENGINE...

IT'S ONLY A GARBAGE TRUCK.

SO, WHO'S THAT CRUMBO IN THE CAB?

IT'S JUDGE DREDD! BUT — WHERE'S THE OTHERS?

CITY GARBAGE.

THERE ARE NO OTHERS. ONE JUDGE IS ENOUGH FOR PUNKS LIKE YOU!

YOU'RE UNDER ARREST!

GET HIM — AAGHH!

I WASN'T TALKING FOR THE GOOD OF MY HEALTH, PAL!

AAAH!

HOW WOULD YOU LIKE A THIRD EYE TO GO WITH THOSE FILED TEETH? THEY SAY IT HELPS YOU TO SEE THE FUTURE!

I—I AIN'T GONNA HAVE NO FUTURE WITH A THIRD EYE! I SURRENDER!

DREDD HANDCUFFED THE CAPTIVES AMONG THE GARBAGE —

LAWBREAKERS **NEED** A DEMONSTRATION OF OUR POWER — AND PERHAPS SO DO THE JUDGES THEMSELVES. MORALE HAS BEEN LOW SINCE CAL — OTHERWISE *TRASH* LIKE THESE PUNKS WOULD NEVER GET OUT OF HAND!

FOLLOW ME AT TEN PACES, TRUCK.

AFFIRMATIVE, SIR.

DO YOU HEAR ME, PUNKS? THIS IS *JUDGE DREDD* AND I'VE COME TO COLLECT THE *GARBAGE!*

HE'S COME ALONE! HE'S GOTTA BE *CRAZY* —

TWO ON THE ROOF — STEEL-TIPPED HIGH-PENETRATION!

AAAAH!

MAN FIRING FROM CORNER WINDOW —

UGGH

HOTSHOT!

DREDD'S LAWGIVER FIRED SIX KINDS OF BULLET. THE HOTSHOT HAD A *HEAT-SEEKING* HOMING HEAD!

AIIEE!

I'M A CHEAP PUNK!

OUTSIDE...

DREDD TO CONTROL. I WANT A TEAM OF AMBULANCES TO ATTEND WOUNDED IN SOUTHSIDE SECTOR 41. NO BACK-UP UNIT NEEDED — IT'S ALL QUIET HERE... REPEAT — ALL QUIET.

DREDD DIRECTED THE TRUCK TOWARDS THE SOUTH MUTIELAND TUNNEL...

H-HEY! DREDD'S DRIVING US INTO M-MUTIELAND!

DANGER! RADIATION ZONE

YOU ARE APPROACHING CURSED EARTH — TRAVEL AT YOUR OWN RISK.

SOUTH MUTIELAND TUNNEL

ON THE OTHER SIDE OF THE TUNNEL —

MEGA-CITY 1 NO ENTRY

AS PUNISHMENT FOR YOUR CRIMES I REMOVE YOUR CITIZENSHIP. YOU WILL NOT BE ALLOWED TO ENTER MEGA-CITY ONE FOR TEN YEARS!

Y-YOU CAN'T DO THIS! THIS PLACE IS A HELL ON EARTH!

GIVE ME TWENTY YEARS — THIRTY — ONLY PLEASE DON'T BANISH ME!

PLEASE! DON'T GO!

IN THE NAME OF MERCY, DON'T DO THIS TO US!

HARSH BUT NECESSARY. LET THEM SERVE AS AN EXAMPLE. LET EVERY MAN KNOW THAT CITIZENSHIP IS A PRIVILEGE — NOT A RIGHT!

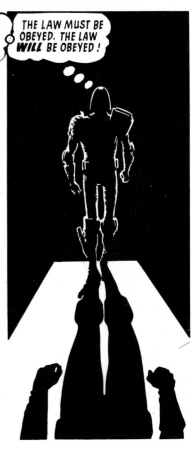

THE LAW MUST BE OBEYED. THE LAW WILL BE OBEYED!

JUDGE DREDD: FEATURING JUDGE DEATH
ISBN 1 84023 386 9

Published by Titan Books,
a division of Titan Publishing Group Ltd.
144 Southwark St
London SE1 0UP
In association with Rebellion

A CIP catalogue record for this title is available from the British Library.

First edition: November 2001
2 4 6 8 10 9 7 5 3 1

Cover illustration by Brian Bolland.

Printed in Italy.

Other *2000 AD* titles now available from Titan Books:

Judge Dredd: Emerald Isle (ISBN: 1 84023 341 9)
The Complete Ballad of Halo Jones (ISBN: 1 84023 342 7)
Zenith: Phase One (ISBN: 1 84023 343 5)
Judge Dredd: Death Aid (ISBN: 1 84023 344 3)
The Complete D.R. & Quinch (ISBN: 1 84023 345 1)
Judge Dredd: Goodnight Kiss (ISBN: 1 84023 346 X)
To order telephone 01536 764 646 ext. 21

What did you think of this book? We love to hear from our readers. Please email us at: readerfeedback@titanemail.com, or write to us at the above address.